Oak
City
Tales

J. ANTON DAVIS

All Points Creative, LLC

Website: JAntonPoetry.com
Instagram: @jantonpoetry
Facebook: J. Anton Poetry
Goodreads: J. Anton Davis

All Points Creative, LLC
P.O. Box 98232
Raleigh, North Carolina 27624

ISBN: 978-1-7355407-2-6 (Paperback)
ISBN: 978-1-7355407-3-3 (eBook)

ONE-FOR-ONE PLEDGE

For every paperback copy of *Oak City Tales* sold in 2021 and 2022, one dollar of each book's royalties received by All Points Creative, LLC, will be donated to one or more organizations helping school-aged children in Raleigh, North Carolina, to improve their reading or writing abilities. These donated funds will be disbursed no later than March 1 of the year following both 2021 and 2022.

The recipient or recipients of these funds will be announced publicly at JAntonPoetry.com and in the J. Anton Poetry email newsletter. You may subscribe to the email newsletter at JAntonPoetry.com.

Thank you for reading and for helping to support young people in Raleigh, North Carolina, as they work to improve their reading and writing abilities.

To my wife, Alexandra,
who has always supported my writing
and who has given me the courage
and strength to not only write this book,
but to put it out into the world,

to my sons, James and Liam,
who I hope will be encouraged by this book
to never stop dreaming as they explore
Raleigh and the rest of our incredible world,

to my friends, family, and anyone who
ever has (or ever will) call Raleigh home.

TABLE OF CONTENTS

Oak
City
Tales

J. ANTON DAVIS

FORWARD

Ever since I was a young boy growing up in Raleigh, North Carolina, I have had an active imagination. One in which horror movie characters might actually be under my bed and pinecones and acorns serve as perfect substitutes for grenades in a game of playground war. One in which thick winter gloves are perfect for shooting lasers from one's hands and creek dams constructed with rocks and dirt can be destroyed by firecracker artillery deployed by enemy forces.

While my imagination, today, does not go to the same places that it did in my childhood – no killer dolls under this guy's bed! – it still gets carried away to far-off places when I am struck by moments of true inspiration or exhilaration. Walking through the woods on a cool fall day or listening to thunder roll on a warm summer night can send my mind into a flurry of activity as it considers the many things that could have happened on a day or night "just like this one."

Having lived almost my entire life in Raleigh, I am a total sucker for its colorful leaves in the fall, its countless trees year round, its museums, its walking trails, and its historic landmarks. While I did grow up outside-the-beltline – gasp! – due to the fact that my Dad worked for over twenty years on either Person Street or Hargett Street, I spent a great deal of my childhood in downtown Raleigh. My siblings and I regularly ran around the State Capitol grounds, ate chips and hotdogs from street vendors, and wandered Fayetteville Street in both its mall and street forms.

Around four-and-a-half years ago, my longstanding love of Raleigh and my lively imagination inspired me to write a book that would create a sense of place, wonder, and legend in the downtown Raleigh area. It is from that desire that the project that would eventually become *Oak City Tales* began, though it took many twists and turns along the way.

I began by writing a book's worth of poems that were set in the downtown area, each telling a complete story that could stand alone, apart from all the others. The stories in those poems described strange and mysterious events, such as trees or inanimate objects coming to life or shifting cobblestones leading to hidden passageways. I loved writing those initial poems and I could picture people of all ages happily reading them in the exact locations where the poems were set. After reading and rereading those poems, however, I decided that in order for the full effect of the stories and legends to be realized, I would need to create and communicate the *why* and the *how* behind each one.

Those original poems and others, as well as the various combined media that explain the *why* and the *how* of those tales, make up the book you now hold in your hands: a fantastic tale of a young man named Emory Alexander whose life changed forever when he picked up what appeared to be a small, uninteresting, run-of-the-mill stone, only to learn that it was in fact enchanted.

I hope that you enjoy reading this book as much as I enjoyed writing it. May it open your mind to the incredible beauty and mystery that are always present in the world around you, whether in reality or as seen through the lens of your imagination.

Oak City Tales

J. ANTON DAVIS

THE MARVELOUS STONE

There is a box that lies unfound,
within a clay-rich, soggy ground,
where once a wall concealed its place,
from all who tread that secret space,
now dirt and rock fill empty lair,
and hillside, whole, protects what's there,

A broken stone concealed by cloth,
encased beyond both rust and moth,
though not because its wooden crypt,
but virtues shown when stone is chipped,
if e'er the dust is grazed or touched,
a font of life, itself, be clutched,
and strength and pow'r be then imbued,
upon the subject, quick or crude,

This stone was once, to all, unknown,
until a drifter, then alone,
picked rock and kindling from the earth,
to show cold bones a fire's worth,
but when the stone and his flint met,
an instant, roaring fire was set,
he leapt back from the blinding glare,

1

of emerald flames that licked the air,

The stone slipped from his startled hand,
and bounced across the timberland,
the scamp, now privy to its power,
dove headlong through bush and flower,
reaching hard with wild eyes,
he caught his tumbling, magic prize,
then, panting from the awkward trial,
slowly he began to smile,

So often pow'r corrupts the mind,
and leaves the sharpest vision blind,
'tis different, not, in this tale told,
but different how the yarns unfold,
so learn the fate of one young dreamer,
sci'ntist, liar, drifter, schemer,
once the man who'd change the world,
until the sails of life unfurled.

THE DIARY OF EMORY ALEXANDER

The 11th Day of October, 1914. Sunday.

I write in my bedroom above Service Drug Store.

Asheville

It has been two years since I found the stone. Two long years of experiment after experiment, seeking ever newer ways to manipulate and direct its raw, unharnessed power.

With a scrape of the stone and a pinch of the right compounds — mixed through extensive trial and error, I must admit — I have learned the appropriate formulas required to make inanimate objects grow, shrink, move about, and float. Furthermore, using similar formulas, I now know how to insert hidden, albeit basic, directives into such objects. For example, I have charmed a spare key to the Drug Store so that it descends from the rooftop and into my hand whenever I return from an errand. This, to be sure, is by no means miraculous. That same concept, however, expanded into larger objects and more useful situations, might change the world as we know it. Yes, much has been accomplished, though much is still to be done.

While working alone, there is only so much one can do. I need another mind to join me in my efforts, aiding me with chemical expertise beyond my exhausted attempts at self-education. Further, the slow evolution of the human specimen has provided me with only two hands, not enough to simultaneously manage both unwieldy subjects and boiling beakers. Developing my floating key trick without a laboratory aid cost me quarts of meticulously prepared formulas. Once doused with the appropriate potion, the keys were less interested in flying into my hand than they were in darting like pinballs from one glass instrument to another. It is for these reasons that my solitary work must soon come to an end.

It has been two years since I first climbed the steps of Service Drug Store, meeting the discriminating, though kind, gaze of Dr. J. Tom Crutchfield as I stumbled through the doorway. At the time, I had not a penny to my name and hardly a penny's worth of energy in my body. Dr. Crutchfield, in his infinite compassion, quickly sized up my tattered clothes and melancholy countenance before asking me those five words that have come to represent the good doctor; "How can I help you?"

Since that day, Dr. Crutchfield has given me food, shelter, and an opportunity to learn about chemical compounds that I could have received from no other person. Though I am three years into adulthood and he is decades beyond that, Dr. Crutchfield and I have treated one another like the family that neither of us had.

It is my great trust in Dr. Crutchfield that leads me to conclude that he must be my first confidante. He will be the first with whom I share the stone's power. His knowledge of chemical compounds knows no equal. With his partnership, there is nothing we won't be able to accomplish. Finally, my long-suffering dreams of discovering and harnessing the stone's deepest potential will be realized.

With Dr. Crutchfield's help, the same scientific brilliance that once sealed my fate as a schoolyard leper will place my name on the lips of every man and woman in the developed world. We will change science and history forever and will hear our surnames discussed alongside those of da Vinci, Newton, and Magellan.

With great perseverance,

E.A.

THE OAK CITY GAZETTE   VOL. 1313

The Oak City Gazette

TUESDAY, OCTOBER 13, 1914

GIANT TOAD ATTACK IN ASHEVILLE

Authorities in Asheville, North Carolina, were left scratching their heads this week after responding to an alleged giant toad attack. The victim of the attack, Dr. J. Tom Crutchfield, runs Service Drug Store, a renowned institution in the scenic mountain town.

Upon hearing screams coming from inside of Dr. Crutchfield's home, located on the 100 block of Arlington Street, his neighbors burst through the front door to help the beleaguered doctor.

Dr. Crutchfield's next-door neighbor, Ms. Abigail Gregory, was the first to enter the home.

"The toad was the size of a black bear," Ms. Gregory recounted. "Dr. Crutchfield screamed bloody murder until we could get his arm out of the toad's mouth, which was in up to his shoulder."

Ms. Gregory reported that it took ten minutes of wrestling the giant toad to free Dr. Crutchfield's arm.

"After that, the toad hopped to the corner of the room, where we surrounded it, waiving lamps and chairs to keep it still until someone could alert the police."

Two hours after the incident occurred, local veterinarian and dogcatcher, Mr. Daniel Dean, arrived at the house.

"The toad that I saw," Mr. Dean explained, "was the size of a large house cat. My best guess is that the toad's unusual size might be linked to chemical fertilizers used by local farmers."

Mr. Dean could not confirm whether the toad had been larger before his arrival, though he believes that to be unlikely.

"I've responded to hundreds of animal attacks in my time. Eye-witness testimony can often be unintentionally exaggerated because of the shock caused by an animal attack. Perceptions and memories can become hazy and twisted together after a traumatic event."

Local reporters have since questioned Dr. Crutchfield about the amphibious altercation, but each has yet to illicit the slightest response. As one reporter noted, the elderly pharmacist remains, "stiff, wide-eyed and pale, appearing to be in a state of shock."

Dr. Jack Northrup, a psychiatrist based in nearby Blowing Rock, North Carolina, has volunteered to examine Dr. Crutchfield, free of charge, with the hope of helping him recover his social faculties.

Service Drug Store will remain closed until Dr. Crutchfield recovers, as Asheville citizens have been unable to locate the young man who helps him to run the store.

THE DIARY OF EMORY ALEXANDER

The 13th Day of October, 1914. Tuesday.

I write in the daytime by train.

Asheville to Raleigh

Dr. Crutchfield got what was coming to him! After all that we have been through, after all the sweat I poured tending his shop each day, his only response to the revelation of my work is to shake that book at me and tell me my research is "unnatural." How could he fail to see the possibilities? It is not about "natural," it is about progress! Real, world-changing progress.

I have never in my life wished to harm Dr. Crutchfield, but when he began to yell about going to the authorities, I had no choice but to splash my growing potion on the closest, most threatening thing I could find. Thankfully, I noticed that toad crouched on his stoop when I first arrived at his front door. Dr. Crutchfield has always hated toads, largely due to their uncanny ability to find hidden routes into the Drug Store and unexpectedly leap out from behind shelving. I can only assume that his fear of the amphibian found new heights yesterday. The leathery thing was eye-level with the doctor when I slammed the door to his house.

As before, it appears that I remain alone in my efforts; an all-too-common theme of my life. How many times must I be rejected by those closest to me to learn that no one can ever truly be trusted? I will not make the same mistake again. I will take this train to Raleigh where I will continue my research and keep to myself. Only when I know that my work is fully prepared will I show others. Even then, those relationships will remain arm's length, focused solely on the work at hand. I have no more patience for the joys of human sentiment, as it seems an inseparable partner of human cruelty and judgment.

With the money I now have, compliments of Dr. Crutchfield's "secret" office safe, I should have no trouble purchasing all the equipment and space I need to continue my work. Who would have guessed that the poor bachelor saved every dollar he ever made? With no young tots to spoil he amassed a small fortune, which has now become a most generous donation to my research.

The train is now passing Greensboro. I have an hour or so to get some rest before I arrive in Raleigh. Then, my work will begin in earnest.

To the future. To progress. To the late Dr. J. Tom

Crutchfield.

With great perseverance,

E.A.

J. ANTON DAVIS

THE BOYLAN HOUSE

Beside the tracks, atop the hill,
a manor slumbers, calm and still,
without an heir to fill the keep,
alone it waits, no eyes to weep,
for long and empty are each day,
since its first owner passed away,
so now it hopes and dreams and waits,
for some new ward to breach the gates,
the house will then be home, again,
a stately hall, a master's den,
a fortress set upon a hill,
for mem'ries good and bad to fill,
till then the lonely floorboards lay,
while in the breeze the cobwebs sway,
awaiting fool as much as sage,
whoe'er would fill the empty cage.

THE OAK CITY GAZETTE   VOL. 1316

The Oak City Gazette

FRIDAY, OCTOBER 16, 1914

MONTFORT HALL PURCHASED

For the first time since 1899, Montfort Hall has a new owner. The Italianate style red brick mansion was most recently owned by the late William Montfort Boylan, namesake of the bourgeoning Boylan Heights neighborhood that now spreads southward from the late owner's estate.

Though architecturally the home is best known for its rotunda, naturally lit by stained glass and held up by four Corinthian columns, Raleigh citizens remember the manor most keenly for the numerous and extravagant dinner parties which were once regularly held there.

"I attended many gatherings there prior to my engagement to Mr. Isaacson," Mrs. Alexandra Isaacson-Heck, whose family has lived in Raleigh for generations, explained. "As a young woman preparing to enter society, there was no more enchanting place to be."

Paperwork filed Wednesday with the Wake County Register of Deeds Office lists Mr. Emory Alexander, a newcomer to Raleigh, as the home's new owner. The filings indicate that Mr. Alexander paid cash for the six thousand square foot manor.

When asked her thoughts about Montfort Hall being owned by someone other than a Raleigh native, Mrs. Isaacson-Heck paused for many moments before answering. "I just hope Mr. Alexander knows what Montfort means to this city and to those of us who spent time there with its original owners. Mr. Alexander has some rather large shoes to fill."

From whence Mr. Alexander hails and to what profession he owes his fortune are unknown. He has yet to be reached for comment.

Since returning to office three years ago, Raleigh Mayor James Johnson has encouraged the City Council to purchase Montfort Hall, believing it to be a unique piece of Raleigh's downtown history that must be protected from disrepair after sitting vacant for so many years. On Thursday, the Mayor's Office released an official statement in response to Mr. Alexander's purchase. "Mayor Johnson is delighted to hear of the purchase of Montfort Hall," the statement read. "He looks forward to meeting Mr. Alexander once he is settled into his new home. Mayor Johnson plans to discuss with Mr. Alexander the high esteem in which Raleigh citizens hold the home, as well as its unique place in the city's rich history."

Rumors circulated four years ago that Mayor Johnson wanted to purchase the storied estate himself, though he has repeatedly denied such claims. An anonymous source at the time explained that the secretive purchase fell through after political opponents of the Mayor threatened to go public with the deal. The whistleblower claimed that the Mayor was planning to pay a reduced purchase price for the home in exchange for future political favors.

Though no record of the

negotiated deal has ever come to light, Mayor Johnson has betrayed its existence on many occasions. Throughout his tenure he has abruptly ended multiple interviews on the subject, and sources close to the Mayor explain that to this day he receives monthly updates on the property.

THE DIARY OF EMORY ALEXANDER

The 18th Day of October, 1914. Sunday.

I write by night in the study.

Raleigh

This new town seems most suitable for the purposes of my work; having explored my local surroundings since I arrived last Tuesday, I am more certain of this fact than when I first came to the conclusion. I am surrounded by great wealth and immense power, both of which I will need in order to confirm my groundbreaking hypothesis: that the base substances of inanimate objects, animals, and even men, can be controlled and manipulated with a drop of an appropriately mixed formula. This formula, of course, being one mixed with the dust of my enchanted stone.

I must continue my experiments as soon as my laboratory is complete. The secretive nature of its location, which requires me to construct the entire complex myself, will cost me weeks of research. This delay, however, cannot be avoided. Were my work to be discovered, without the proper explanation of its properties and purpose, it might be as poorly received as it was by Dr. Crutchfield. Raleigh is a progressive city, to be sure, but many long-held beliefs run through the very soil of this state, as indomitable as the red clay that fills the ground. In this respect, it is with great fortune that the considerable basement of my new home is not listed on any recorded deed, and that there is room for further expansion into the earth surrounding it.

With all hope, in a month's time I will once again light my laboratory burners, each blue flame the catalyst for a fantastic new discovery.

With great perseverance and much hope,

E.A.

P.S. - Mayor Johnson's unannounced and rather odd visit to my home yesterday afternoon was a good reminder that I must be ever-vigilant of prying eyes. Though I did not allow him past the entryway, the nosy glad-hander spied every visible corner and crevice of the foyer as Sherlock Holmes might have done while investigating a London bank robbery. Mayor Johnson is clearly displeased with my presence at Montfort. His unique fondness for the property, as I understand it from the local papers, means I will have to keep as watchful an eye on him as he does on me.

Interoffice Memorandum

Chief Cecil Miller

Raleigh Police Department

Tuesday, October 20, 1914

Good morning:

Mayor Johnson has a special assignment for us. Not only the substance of the assignment, but even its existence, is to remain confidential.

A newcomer to town has bought Montfort Hall, the red brick mansion that sits at the corner of Boylan Avenue and Mountford Avenue. While there have been no reports of suspicious activity at the home, the Mayor is uneasy about the new owner, a Mr. Emory Alexander. He mentioned that during a visit he made to the home this weekend in order to welcome Mr. Alexander to Raleigh, Mr. Alexander appeared abnormally secretive and would not even allow him past the threshold of the home. No active surveillance is required, but officers assigned to the Boylan Heights neighborhood should speak with Mr. Alexander whenever the opportunity presents itself.

I thank you in advance for your attention to this assignment. It needs no repeating for the more senior members of the Department that Montfort Hall has always held a special place in the Mayor's heart. Let's not let anything happen to it under our watch.

Be safe out there and remember the badge you wear.

Chief Cecil Miller

Cecil Miller

RALEIGH POLICE DEPARTMENT

IF YOU ARE NOT A MEMBER OF THE RALEIGH POLICE DEPARTMENT, RETURN THIS DOCUMENT TO THE NEAREST POLICE STATION IMMEDIATELY

THE OAK CITY GAZETTE   VOL. 1326

The Oak City Gazette

MONDAY, OCTOBER 26, 1914

ASHEVILLE TOAD ATTACK

While a police investigation focused on a giant toad attack may seem like the plot of a Halloween fiction novel, it is a current reality for one North Carolina mountain town.

Nearly two weeks ago, reports out of Asheville, North Carolina described a man having been attacked by a toad the size of a small bear. The victim of the attack, Dr. J. Tom Crutchfield, escaped the encounter with only minor scrapes and bruises, though his mental faculties were greatly affected.

The doctor has been unable to communicate since the incident, presumably due to the shock sustained from the attack. After multiple meetings with a local psychiatrist, Dr. Crutchfield is finally speaking again, and the details he is sharing of the altercation are nothing short of incredible.

Dr. Crutchfield told investigators that his shop assistant, Dillon Westwood, orchestrated the attack. His memory of the incident is severely fragmented, but Dr. Crutchfield recalls having an argument with Mr. Westwood that ended when the assailant threw a large toad at him that would not stop growing.

Investigators with the Asheville Police Department are uncertain of how to proceed. It would likely be the first time in the state's history for an individual to be charged with what Asheville officers are affectionally calling, "assault-by-toad," so investigators are hesitant to formally charge Mr. Westwood until more is known about the situation.

One of the most interesting wrinkles in this already outlandish story is that the person of interest, Mr. Dillon Westwood, is not named Dillon Westwood at all. Through initial investigation, it has become clear that this name was a false name provided to Dr. Crutchfield, though as it is the only known alias at this time, it is still being used by police for investigative purposes.

Without a valid name, Asheville detectives are left with few options of how best to pursue the alleged assailant. Based upon Dr. Crutchfield's knowledge of the man known as Mr. Westwood, a sketch has been released to local and surrounding communities to see what leads may surface.

Authorities believe it is likely that the suspect is still in the greater Asheville area or has fled west into Tennessee.

Raleigh Police Chief Cecil Miller has urged all citizens to report any suspicious activity that may be linked to the Asheville attack, though a statement released from his office stated that the Department has no reason to believe the suspect is anywhere near the capital city.

Interoffice Memorandum

Chief Cecil Miller

Raleigh Police Department

Tuesday, October 27, 1914

Good morning:

As previously mentioned, we've received a statewide alert from Asheville reporting an assault upon a local citizen there. The suspect's true name is unknown at this time, though he may be traveling under the alias of Dillon Westwood. He is said to be roughly five feet, eight inches tall, with unkempt, dark hair, dark eyes, and a thin frame. He is estimated to be twenty or twenty-one years of age, though that has not yet been confirmed.

An alleged assault involving a giant mountain toad is not a typical report we receive in our office, however, I assured Asheville's police chief that we would keep our eyes out for anything suspicious. While it is likely that the suspect is nowhere near the Raleigh area, we must remain vigilant.

Be safe out there today and remember the badge you wear.

Chief Cecil Miller

Cecil Miller

RALEIGH POLICE DEPARTMENT

IF YOU ARE NOT A MEMBER OF THE RALEIGH POLICE DEPARTMENT, RETURN THIS DOCUMENT TO THE NEAREST POLICE STATION IMMEDIATELY

THE DIARY OF EMORY ALEXANDER

The 13th Day of November, 1914. Friday.

I write at dawn in the kitchen.

Raleigh

The slow growth of my work is finally picking up speed. Though incomplete, my laboratory has hummed for two weeks' time with burning flames and frothing beakers. Colorful concoctions of all kinds boil at all corners of my basement, creating an otherworldly aura of blue, green, and red light in the dark space. At times I feel as if I stand among some unknown constellation of a far-off galaxy, one in which each star is prepared to do my bidding whenever called upon. With every new experiment, I can't help but feel that the entire world lies at my feet, my next discovery waiting eagerly behind that thin veil of scientific experiment.

Though still humble progress, I have begun to test my formulas upon local species of insects and arachnids. The findings have been fascinating. Each experiment is rich with new information, proving that even the slightest addition or subtraction to a formula can change the results entirely.

Just the other day I managed to combine a growing potion with an acceleration potion, causing a tiny wolf spider to grow to the size of my hand and erratically scuttle throughout the laboratory. It eventually found a resting place in the eves beside the staircase leading to the main house. I have named it Tom, after Dr. Crutchfield. While the Gazette has alerted me to the good doctor's survival in Asheville, it still seemed fitting to honor the de facto loss of my once-trusted mentor. My newly christened Tom, while menacing, seems to understand that I mean him no harm and has so far kept to himself. I will continue to observe him and record my findings.

Since arriving in Raleigh, only slightly have I proceeded to testing more complex creatures than arachnids and insects, and not by original design. I learned after only a short time on Boylan Hill that the capital city has a considerable population of stray dogs. Members of this feral pack regularly wander the edge of town near Montfort in search of a generously shared — or ill-gotten! — meal. While I have provided many a biscuit, doused each time with some newly concocted potion, none of the subjects have yet returned that I might record my findings. This fact seems odd, however, as often I rise to meet a lonesome howl or scratch at my front door, only to find an empty stoop.

Though findings are few, I am encouraged and hopeful with the present state of my work. Furthermore, in only a few days' time the additions to my laboratory will be complete.

With great perseverance, and no small amount of patience,

E.A.

THE HOUNDS OF OAKWOOD

At night, when wand'ring in the still
and silent Oakwood streets,
if one would pause and dare to hear,
an echoed call repeats,

At first the soft and gentle sound
of one abandoned dog,
but growing always louder till,
begins the dialogue,

Barks and bays of every kind
will pierce the trembling air,
though searching everything in sight,
you will not know from where,

The raps of paws upon the street
will sound their swift advance,
till unseen teeth snap at your feet,
though landing not a glance,

You'll kick and swing and yell and shout,
but all to no avail,
you won't connect with any snout,

31

with any paw or tail,

The fever pitch of wild hounds
will swell against your senses,
till all at once the onslaught stops
and all the noise condenses,

One lonely bark will join the drum
still pounding in your chest,
to mark the threat of Oakwood hounds
who never sleep or rest,

Be warned that day of what you've heard,
let not it happen twice,
for on the second meeting there
the charmed will loose their vice.

THE SEVEN LEGG'D SPIDER OF BOYLAN BRIDGE

Beside the tracks, within the hill,
there is a creature lurking still,
that once was shot and left to die,
but never did its body lie,

Beneath the dirt, its wounds did heal
and left it hungry for a meal,
so, tasting flesh, and vengeance, too,
it ate the man whose shotgun blew
its leg to bits that fateful night,
when on the hill it did alight,
to make a feast of wand'ring sheep
whose farmer it believed asleep,

Had shotgun spray been true and right
we'd have no need for fear or fright,
but as one leg, alone, was lost,
the death of many be the cost,

Ten times a man in size and strength,
with seven legs to reach its length,
its eyes like fire, its fangs like ice,

its web a gripping, crushing vice,

Surviving, still, it roams at night,
while full of hate and appetite,
be not a meal within the ridge,
beware the spider of Boylan Bridge.

Interoffice Memorandum

Chief Cecil Miller

Raleigh Police Department

Sunday, November 22, 1914

Good morning:

We have an urgent and sensitive APB, which I know will not surprise those of you that have worked the night shift the past few weeks.

We have received regular reports of a pack of animals destroying property and attacking homeowners and pets in the downtown area. The group of animals is believed to be feral dogs, wolves, or foxes, and only seems to attack at night. While we have received nearly ten related reports, no one has been able to lay eyes on the animals.

Tonight, our Special Response Team will patrol local neighborhoods for any sign of the pack. If anyone would like to join them and earn a little overtime pay, be my guest. The Mayor has emphasized the vital importance of catching these animals before any kind of rabies scare starts to circulate and negatively affect downtown businesses.

To those on the SRT: remember to wear thick clothing to avoid any kind of contamination if bitten or scratched.

Contact me with any new information.

Chief Cecil Miller

Cecil Miller

RALEIGH POLICE DEPARTMENT

IF YOU ARE NOT A MEMBER OF THE RALEIGH POLICE DEPARTMENT, RETURN THIS DOCUMENT TO THE NEAREST POLICE STATION IMMEDIATELY

THE DIARY OF EMORY ALEXANDER

The 9th Day of December, 1914. Wednesday.

I write by night at my laboratory desk.

Raleigh

After rapid acceleration, my research and experiments have slowed as of late. This delay is due entirely to the fact that the expansion of my laboratory has exceeded my wildest expectations!

Two weeks ago, while digging out the dirt and clay behind which I believed would be the last few feet of my workshop, my pickaxe struck hard against a firm object. Assuming I had merely hit a particularly chilled piece of November earth, I swung again, this time with added force. Based upon the sparks and the rather loud "clang" that erupted from the wall, I knew that some metal surface must be concealed there. After an hour of cautious digging with hand picks and chisels, fearing that I would burst some underground water pipe, I unearthed a small, black door.

The door's top edge stood at the height of my chin, while its iron-ring handle hung in front of my chest. There were no markings to denote the door's purpose, though the dirt wall surrounding it was dry, showing no signs that water might await me on the other side. With my fears tempered by my initial assessment, I began a short and futile struggle to open the small door, yielding only an enormous amount of perspiration. Finally, after two more hours of meticulous scraping between the door and its casing, I was able to wrench it open. Before me was an empty, narrow, insufferably dark tunnel.

Over the next few weeks, I slowly and methodically

wandered the tunnel, candle and compass in hand, mapping each step. It took only an hour of exploration to learn that the tunnel I had entered was just a small part of a maze of similarly constructed passageways. Each turn was as dark as the last. The air was dry and seemed to have not been disturbed for many years, creating an almost tangible staleness. As one might expect in such a desolate environment, there was no living thing to be found. Not even an earthworm.

Based upon my subsequent expeditions, the tunnels appear to be part of an abandoned sewer line which stretches under the entirety of downtown Raleigh. This was made clear to me as I discovered nearly twenty sets of iron ladders leading up to long-forgotten manholes around the city. Though it was impossible to dislodge each from their holdings, at least ten eventually broke free.

Then, with only a slight lift of each iron cap, I found I was able to gaze upon the streets beneath which I walked. First, West Street, then Harrington, and so on.

Based upon my many trips through the tunnels, it appears that I have nearly completed the mapping of the underground labyrinth. It has been a laborious and time-intensive project, but I could think of no better asset to my research than secluded, uninhibited access to the entire city proper!

With great perseverance,

E.A.

P.S. - I must confirm the local train schedule prior to my next expedition. I recently found myself beneath the tracks when a locomotive came into town. Based upon the shards of piping that fell upon my head, the drainage system must not retain the same strength it boasted at its original construction. I must take precautions to avoid becoming "exhibit one" in the catalogue discussing the dangers of wandering through abandoned, crumbling tunnels with trains overhead.

J. ANTON DAVIS

THE OAKS OF NASH AND MOORE

The oaks, the oaks of Nash and Moore
stand proudly in their earthen floor,
though not, in truth, a docile corps,
but soldiers primed and braced for war,

For many years before this day
a magic man passed by this way,
and needing guards without delay
he cast a spell on every spray,

Without a moment more, each shoot
burst forth to life with one pursuit,
to heed the mystic piper's flute
whene'er he calls them from the root,

For deep beneath the grassy ground
a secret lies, today, unfound,
that were it sought the trees be bound
to fight to death and trumpet's sound,

So e'er they wait and watch their keep,
they never tire, they never sleep,
those int'rested in what lies deep,

prepare to fight, prepare to weep.

THE DIARY OF EMORY ALEXANDER

The 18th Day of January, 1915. Monday.

I write at dawn over breakfast.

Raleigh

My research is moving along splendidly and at breakneck speed. I have now mastered my work with complex animals, experimenting mostly upon dogs and cats. Aside from these common specimens, I have experimented on an occasional bovine or other farm animal. Such exotic experimentation is considerably rarer, however, as it is difficult to find such expensive subjects lost and wandering near my property line.

On only one occasion have I been approached by a desperate farmer in search of his livestock; his rooster was "nowhere to be found," of course. In all honesty, however, the bird could have been standing on the farmer's shoulder and we would not have known it. The poor creature shrunk to the size of a ladybug the instant I dripped my shrinking potion on its head, and I have not seen it since.

Apart from living creatures, I have also begun dabbling with potions that might be used upon stone, metal, and wood that could make each separate material perform an act in unison. Though the flying keys were a great feat of my earlier research, I must learn how to create a symphony with my potions, not merely a solo performance. As I have written many times, small successes in the laboratory may not appear revolutionary, but expand the proven concept and one might just change the world.

I will continue my research on these "collaborative" potions with much excitement. Once I perfect my methods, these experiments will join the others in the greater laboratory of downtown Raleigh. Each new discovery must be slowly shared with the public, lest I arouse and startle their southern sensitivities. While I am of southern birth, myself, I do not share my brethren's distaste for change or for science. In fact, I am very fond of both!

With great perseverance,

E.A.

THE OAK CITY GAZETTE   VOL. 1445

The Oak City Gazette

MONDAY, FEBRUARY 22, 1915

FLOATING TRAINS AND STREETCARS

What was first believed to be a child's tall tale has now grown into the talk of the town.

Reports have become more frequent that both rail and street cars in the downtown Raleigh area have been seen floating upon airborne tracks. No one has yet been able to photograph these strange occurrences, but Raleigh Mayor James Johnson has personally requested that all local publications assign a photographer to do just that.

Few passengers of these enchanted rail and street cars have been interviewed, as many are too disturbed by the incident to recount their experience in detail.

"It happened so fast," said one passenger, Ms. Faye Hershey of Woodbridge Court. "I saw a faint blue light outside of the train's window, then felt a slight drop in my stomach."

It was at that time, Ms. Hershey explained, that her train car and the other connected cars rose ten feet into the air upon floating tracks. After only seconds of this elevated travel, there was a calm descent, the extinguishing of the blue light, and an otherwise uninterrupted journey to Union Station.

Mr. Liam Nittolo, a clerk at the downtown G&S Department Store, described a similar experience while riding a streetcar to work last Thursday morning.

"After we lifted into the air, I was looking straight into the second-floor windows of every building on Fayetteville Street," Mr. Nittolo said. "By the time I had shaken my head and rubbed my eyes, we were back on the ground. I thought I had lost my marbles until I heard that others had seen the same thing."

Though City of Raleigh engineers have inspected the train and streetcar tracks at locations where these floating incidents have been reported, none have found anything out of the ordinary. Engineers from both Carolina Power and Light Company and the Southern and Seaboard Airline Railroad, the companies that maintain Raleigh's streetcar and railroad tracks, respectively, reported the same.

Mayor Johnson has assured citizens that City of Raleigh staff will continue to perform inspections until the geneses of these reports are discovered.

"We will keep inspecting the affected tracks," Mayor Johnson told reporters last Friday, "until we have solved this mystery or these reports have stopped entirely."

Citizens whose livelihoods depend on trains and streetcars hope that a solution to these problems comes quickly. Since these reports have surfaced, the daily passenger rates for both forms of transportation have dropped nearly fifty percent. Due to the related decrease in downtown visitors, local workers are worried that their jobs will be gone before summer if something is not done soon.

FLOATING TRACKS

The tracks that carry man and ware
to Union Station floor,
rest cold and black within the ground,
a lifeless chain, naught more,
this would be true were tie or timber
free from heedless tests,
but potion poured upon them both
demands that neither rests,

As train cars pass beside the hill
once filled with boiling froth,
the tracks give rise as if a serpent
craning for the broth,
the steel wheels forge ahead as though
undaunted by the shift,
though naught is lost upon the trav'lers
quaking from the lift,

They shriek and jump and line the windows,
petrified with fear,
till moments later, without warning,
down the train cars veer,
without a noise the tracks return

to etchings in the ground,
to lie as though 'twere always so,
no life, no lift, no sound,

Now every turn around the bend
below the fated hill,
brings rise to tie and timber, both,
all never to be still.

THE OAK CITY GAZETTE   VOL. 1468

The Oak City Gazette

WEDNESDAY, MARCH 17, 1915

CHILDREN GO MISSING AT NEW CITY MARKET

Adding to the peculiar happenings that have befallen the Raleigh area in recent months, the new City Market at Moore Square has turned into a place of unexplained disappearances.

On many different occasions, shoppers have become separated from their children soon after arriving at the market. These parents describe looking away for only a moment before realizing their child was missing.

All but one of the children, whom local investigators are still searching for, were located within hours. The location of their recovery, however, has authorities puzzled. Each child was found wandering at various locations on the outskirts of the downtown area, all more than half a mile away from the City Market. The Raleigh Police Department is investigating the multiple disappearances, though sources within the Department report that investigators are struggling to make sense of everything.

Raleigh Police Chief Cecil

Miller hopes that the conversations he has had and will continue to have with many of the children who went missing will soon yield fruit in the investigation.

"Those children that are old enough to describe the experience," Chief Miller explained, "have mentioned a falling sensation, followed by hours of walking through dark, empty tunnels."

Chief Miller's investigation team noted in a recent report that the area surrounding the new market does not include any known entryways into the city's former sewer system. This fact confuses investigators, however, as each child interviewed has independently reported emerging from tunnels linked to that very system.

"We aren't really sure what to believe," Chief Miller added, "as one young boy claims to have found a locked iron door in the tunnel with candlelight and symphonic music coming from the other side. It is

additions like these that lead us to believe we must take each story with a grain of salt, understanding that fear and disorientation may taint the details we are provided."

As of late last night, one child is still missing from a trip to the market yesterday afternoon. The child's name is Les Hollenbach. He is eight years old, four feet and four inches tall, with brown hair and brown eyes. Les was last seen wearing a white ball cap, red shirt, and blue jeans. If anyone has information regarding his whereabouts, you are urged to contact the Raleigh Police Department using the main switchboard.

These vexing disappearances have dampened the excitement that has surrounded the new City Market since its October 1st grand opening. The previous City Market location was shut down following continual reports of an uncontrollable rat infestation that led citizens to question the market's sanitation.

Mayor Johnson promised supporters for two years that he would construct the new City Market, and he cannot be thrilled at this early blow to the project's success.

In a recent press release, the Mayor's Office attempted to reassure citizens of the capital city.

"The City is putting its best detectives and public servants on the case, so there is no reason to be alarmed," the statement read. "With that said, please do not forget to stop by the City Market as you prepare for the Easter holiday! Vendors are ready and excited to meet your every need."

Notwithstanding Mayor Johnson's optimism, only time will tell whether Raleigh citizens share the Mayor's confidence regarding the future success of the fledgling market.

THE COBBLES OF CITY MARKET

When walking 'mong the cobblestones
that lay just south of Moore,
look sharp, for every step you take
could sink the petrous floor,

For many years before this day
the stones were given charge,
to take their master 'neath the streets
when e'er the want was large,

He'd tap his feet upon the rocks,
first here, then there, just so,
completing, then, a secret code
to take him fast below,

In unison the stones would drop
to form a spiral stair,
then out of sight the scamp would flee
to tunnel, then to lair,

The stones would snap back into place,
this movement, undetected,
to lie, again, a molded heap

of ballast stone rejected,

Throughout the years a startled few
have stumbled down these stairs,
each did not know their tapping feet
would catch them unawares,

These wand'ring souls would oft emerge
where drainage pipes are found,
with wild eyes of someone freed
from labyrinth underground,

But some have wandered
ne'er to feel another drop of light,
they searched until they could no more
then joined the tunnel's night,

So, if you stroll the cobbled streets
that lay just south of Moore,
mind every step and linger not
if darkness you abhor.

Interoffice Memorandum

Chief Cecil Miller

Raleigh Police Department

Thursday, March 18, 1915

Good morning:

I cannot stress enough the importance
of this message and our current work.

The Mayor is furious. As you all
know, a child has been missing from
the new City Market since
Tuesday. While I know many of you
have not slept much the past few days
due to the spike in missing person
cases, everyone must remain on duty
until we find the last missing child.

As stated in previous memos, Les
Hollenbach is four feet, four inches
tall and was last seen wearing a white
cap, red shirt, and blue jeans.

Overtime pay can be worked out as soon as Les is found. Anyone submitting overtime paperwork before that time will be given permanent time off from this Department.

Notwithstanding our primary focus, Detectives Vargas and Aneja will be assigned to citizen intake. We have received over three hundred reports since last fall regarding strange and mysterious happenings in our city. We must find the thread that ties them all together. Every officer that is approached by a member of the public with an outlandish story is to take down the individual's information and refer them to the intake team for further questioning.

Let's find that missing boy and end the chaos in our city! The safety of everyone in our community, as well as each one of our jobs, is at stake.

Find that boy!

Chief Cecil Miller

Cecil Miller

RALEIGH POLICE DEPARTMENT

IF YOU ARE NOT A MEMBER OF THE RALEIGH POLICE DEPARTMENT, RETURN THIS DOCUMENT TO THE NEAREST POLICE STATION IMMEDIATELY

THE DIARY OF EMORY ALEXANDER

The 21st Day of March, 1915. Sunday.

I write at dawn in the laboratory.

Raleigh

I cannot believe I have been so reckless! Candles and music? What does a scientist need with candles and music, when given the opportunity to change history?

It has been twelve hours since I heard banging on the iron door of my laboratory. Fortunately, I have not heard another sound since. I was just about to place a drop of invisibility potion onto an unhappy green lizard when the first fist struck. "Hello, this is the Raleigh Police Department! Is there anyone there?"

How in all creation did they come to my laboratory door?

Thanks to the Gazette, I knew that Chief Miller and his

officers might be searching the tunnels, but I did not

expect them to wander anywhere near my laboratory.

Fortunately, I was able to stop the record player and snuff

out my candles just before backup arrived to join the

officer banging on my door. After attempting to explain

the faint light he had seen and the music he had heard,

the other members of the team dismissed the officer's

report almost instantaneously. "Thompson, go home and

get some rest. You've been down in these tunnels too

long," was all the officer-in-charge said.

Were "Thompson's" arguments of sincerity not so pathetic,

his team may have believed him. As it stood, however, he

sounded as exhausted as he did delirious. Fortunately for

me, the group of officers moved on after only a few

minutes' rest at the door. It seems that no one connected

Thompson's report with a similar story that Chief Miller shared recently in the Gazette regarding testimony from one of the missing City Market children.

From now on, I will work only by the light of my burners. Further, the luxuries of orchestral music must be reserved for the main house. Such creature comforts have no place within a secret laboratory.

With great perseverance, and even greater caution!
E.A.

THE OAK CITY GAZETTE   VOL. 1480

The Oak City Gazette

MONDAY, MARCH 29, 1915

SPECIAL REPORT
INTERVIEW WITH THE CHIEF OF POLICE

Amid the daily reports of outlandish and unbelievable occurrences in the capital city, there are the rare rays of sunshine that peak through the clouds.

As of eight days ago, Raleigh Police Chief Cecil Miller and his officers found the last child who had gone missing from the new City Market shopping area. The young boy, Les Hollenbach, was found exhausted and hungry, but otherwise unharmed.

"Ten days ago, the Department developed a task force," Chief Miller explained, "called the 'Tunnel Team.' The team led daily searches through the abandoned underground tunnels from which the other missing children had emerged."

Using decades-old maps provided by City of Raleigh engineers, the Tunnel Team was able to slowly and methodically work through the tunnel system to eventually locate young Mr. Hollenbach.

"Our team worked tirelessly

until little Les was found last Sunday," Chief Miller recounted. "Each member of the Tunnel Team has only just returned from some well-deserved time off."

Over the past few weeks, Chief Miller, in collaboration with Raleigh Mayor James Johnson's Office, has also developed a special task force specifically assigned to receive and process community complaints.

"Calls to the Department have nearly quadrupled over the past five months," Chief Miller explained. "We are fortunate that the City Council was willing to allocate emergency funds to the Department when they realized how strained our resources have been throughout the current crisis."

The Mayor's Office recently released a statement confirming this allocation of funds, calling it the, "Mayor Johnson City Relief Package."

Chief Miller has urged all citizens to remain vigilant in the coming weeks, alerting the Raleigh Police Department whenever the need arises, especially to report strange or unexplainable events.

"In order to keep the community safe," Chief Miller concluded, "we need everyone to be on guard. While the mayhem seems to have an epicenter of downtown Raleigh, all citizens must be on high alert until we get a handle on the situation."

Having a handle on the current chaos in Raleigh is a milestone that all citizens of the capital city hope to reach as quickly as possible.

THE DIARY OF EMORY ALEXANDER

The 28th Day of April, 1915. Wednesday.

I write by night in the study.

Raleigh

It appears that the people of Raleigh have grown to appreciate my genius, though they do not know it is mine.

Scores of citizens report daily to newspapers and authorities of strange occurrences around the city. They are wowed by unseen animals and exhilarated by flying trains. Some have even organized a "community watch" team to keep an eye on local railways. These groups, I have read, seem to be a blend of those who have sincere safety concerns and those exhilarated by the idea of seeing a train fly. If they only knew that flying trains will be considered mere child's play when compared to the advancements brought on by the coming scientific revolution!

Once the people of Raleigh realize that my potions are the catalysts of these wonders, I will receive overnight celebrity. Every man, woman, and child will have want of some specific potion. The scientific community will revere me and the public at large will throw their support and financing behind any project I propose.

This swift notoriety will be vital to the ultimate success of my work, though not because I hold important the fickle opinions of the citizens of Raleigh. No, their support is vital because I fear that without it my efforts may be stamped out by those of the same ilk as Dr. Crutchfield. Once my research is revealed to the public, the momentum of excitement surrounding it will be unstoppable. The cries of any critics will be drowned out by the cheers of the masses, those who see hope for their own lives in the findings of my research.

There is still much to be done, but the day draws near when the veil of secrecy surrounding my work will be thrust aside.

With great perseverance!

E.A.

THE OAK CITY GAZETTE   VOL. 1539

The Oak City Gazette

THURSDAY, MAY 27, 1915

LOCAL SCIENTIST TO GIVE PRESENTATION

While slightly unconventional in this modern age, a local scientist has convinced a group of state lawmakers to hear a public presentation regarding his research. The scientist is Mr. Emory Alexander of Montfort Hall.

Mr. Alexander has been living in Raleigh since he purchased Montfort Hall in October of last year. Nothing is currently known of his academic training or tutelage, or from whence Mr. Alexander hailed prior to arriving in Raleigh. These and many more questions will likely be answered by Mr. Alexander at his upcoming presentation.

The event, which is open to the public, will be held in the House Chamber of the State Capitol on the 10th of June, Thursday, at seven o'clock in the evening.

While the excitement and anticipation surrounding the presentation has been growing rapidly since its recent announcement, almost nothing is known of the subject of the talk. Mr. Alexander cannot be reached for comment and no legislator will admit to sponsoring the event, though many confess plans to attend.

One lawmaker, who wished to remain anonymous, claims that Mr. Alexander promised he and others that the presentation would be, "the spark of a new scientific revolution," adding that, "all will be made clear on June 10th."

As one might expect of such a mysterious event, not every legislator is convinced of its value. Notwithstanding this skepticism, however, no member of the House or Senate has publicly opposed the presentation.

Legislators appear to be buckling under recent public pressure to allow more citizen input into the legislative process, so it appears that Mr. Alexander has won the chance to be the first subject of this great societal experiment.

Among many notable state and local leaders, sources say Governor Craig may also be in attendance.

THE DIARY OF EMORY ALEXANDER

The 10th Day of June, 1915. Thursday.

I write at noon in the garden.

Raleigh

While I do not make a habit of spending extended periods of time outdoors, I cannot help but write at this moment in the open air. The garden seemed to me a perfect spot to calm my nerves before tonight's presentation. There is a slight breeze, made more pronounced by the fanning potion I poured on my magnolia tree for added wind. The warm June air seems poised with the expectation of summer, just as I await my presentation like a hound on a leash, the scent of fox in the air and the trumpets rising to the signalers' lips.

Tonight, I will unveil my work to the outside world and, in

doing so, will change the course of human history. I can only imagine that Edison felt as I do now before he unveiled the incandescent lightbulb, and Galileo before sharing the mysteries of the solar system. No more days and nights experimenting beneath the earth, hiding like a varmint in its hole. Soon I will be liberated, my eyes adjusting to the light of day as every resource this state has to offer is thrust upon me.

Thankfully, tonight's presentation within the House Chamber was easier to arrange than expected, notwithstanding the great pains I took to ensure my request would be granted. I was right to target Representative Howley. The Gazette has made clear that his reelection hopes are dependent upon him proving that he in fact accomplishes work while in Raleigh. Unfortunately for Representative Howley, smoking cigars in the Legislative Library only greases the wheels of progress when the participants of such sessions are focused on some legislative agenda. As he appears to have never had such a focus, I rightly suspected that the good Representative would gladly jump at the opportunity to sponsor such a promising presentation as mine. After tonight, who knows, he may one day be president!

As one rises to the top, there must inevitably be those who hang from his coat tails. Why shouldn't Representative Howley take mine as high as he can go? Goodness knows he won't reach the top by any other means!

With immense expectation,

E.A.

Interoffice Memorandum

Chief Cecil Miller

Raleigh Police Department

Thursday, June 10, 1915

Good morning:

We have been asked by state officials to help secure the State Capitol tonight for a scientific presentation being given by Mr. Emory Alexander of Montfort Hall.

Governor Craig, Mayor Johnson, and other notable officials will be in attendance, so it is vital that we be wary of every man, woman, and child in the audience. We don't want anyone to use this event as an occasion to air grievances or settle scores.

We will need two officers at each entrance and five inside the House Chamber where the presentation will take place. Mayor Johnson has also asked that we keep a special eye on Mr. Alexander, as we still do not know what his presentation entails. While the Mayor understands that the safety of attendees will be our first priority, he is adamant that Mr. Alexander be our second.

Regardless of what happens, the entire state will read about this presentation in tomorrow's paper, so let's make our work count.

Be safe, tonight, and be vigilant.

Chief Cecil Miller

Cecil Miller

RALEIGH POLICE DEPARTMENT

IF YOU ARE NOT A MEMBER OF THE RALEIGH POLICE DEPARTMENT, RETURN THIS DOCUMENT TO THE NEAREST POLICE STATION IMMEDIATELY

THE OAK CITY GAZETTE   VOL. 1554

The Oak City Gazette

FRIDAY, JUNE 11, 1915

ODD SCIENTIST FALLS FLAT

After days of growing anticipation, local tinkerer Mr. Emory Alexander fell flat last night during a scientific presentation in the State House Chamber.

Hundreds attended the mysterious event, touted as a presentation that would revolutionize medicine, industry, and commerce throughout the state and world. In almost perfect juxtaposition with the excitement surrounding the talk, Mr. Alexander's great reveal turned out to be nothing more than a farce.

At a quarter past seven o'clock yesterday evening, fifteen minutes after the event was scheduled to begin, Mr. Alexander had still not appeared from behind his magician's curtain. The audience, including such high-profile attendees as Governor Craig, Raleigh Mayor James Johnson, and numerous state legislators, waited quietly and anxiously for any sign that the presentation would soon begin.

At half past seven, the crowd became restless. Men impatiently checked their pocket watches while women whispered none-too-quiet criticisms among their parties. Nothing was heard from Mr. Alexander but the occasional clink of glass against glass coming from behind his curtain.

At seven forty-five, without notice or cue, Mr. Alexander stepped out from his mysterious hiding spot and into the view of the audience. It was at that time that the presentation began, in the most generous sense of the word.

After belting out a brief and generous introduction of himself and his purported work with scientific potions, Mr. Alexander thrust aside his bed-sheet curtain, only to catch the curtain's edge on the corner of his newly revealed worktable. In an instant, scores of fastidiously arranged beakers filled with green, red, and blue concoctions went flying into the air. Each slimy brew crashed hard upon the floor of the House Chamber, sending those attendees in the immediate vicinity running from their seats.

As Mr. Alexander frantically attempted to salvage the contents of even a single beaker, he implored the crowd to wait. "This will only take a moment!" he was heard shouting.

Largely spurred by the oddity of the scene, as well as the spectacular and immediate conclusion of the presentation, onlookers who had not fled the falling potions erupted into a crescendo of laughter.

As the cacophony of snickers slowly faded, members of the audience filed out of the chamber, exchanging jokes and pleasantries as they went. Some threw handkerchiefs in Mr. Alexander's direction, at once offering both help with beaker clean-up and symbolic, bemused condolences for the grand public humiliation he had just suffered.

Mr. Alexander was last seen

by attendees with his hands and knees buried into the now colorfully soaked carpet, staring blankly at the floor.

Some audience members also reported seeing an elderly man confront Mr. Alexander, berating him while shaking in his face what appeared to be a rather large toad. Fearing that the situation would escalate into violence, these observers left the room before hearing the nature of the dispute.

It is unclear whether Mr. Alexander will attempt to reschedule his presentation, but it seems unlikely that state or local leaders would now oblige such a request.

Democratic State House Representative Edward Howley of Dare County, the now-known sponsor of the presentation, has yet to be reached for comment. After growing speculation that the once-powerful representative would not win reelection next year, this new blemish on his record almost guarantees that his days as a lawmaker are numbered.

THE DIARY OF EMORY ALEXANDER

The 11th Day of June, 1915. Friday.

I write at dawn in the laboratory.

Raleigh

Finished! They're all finished! I will ruin each person who laughed and sneered while months of my work soaked into the House carpet! If only my potions had been fully mixed, their laughter would have quickly turned into screams. I am not sure that Governor Craig's smirk would have lasted so long had the floor begun to disappear under his feet! If only.

And Dr. Crutchfield; how did that old man even get to Raleigh! I must have let slip once or twice that I dreamed of traveling here. Thank goodness I had one vile of fully mixed potion in my breast pocket. Had I splashed the good doctor even a second later, someone may have heard his tirade about the toad attack. If that had happened, it would have been impossible to leave the Capitol without handcuffs on my wrists. I am still not sure whether I splashed Dr. Crutchfield with a potion mixed to make stones stack upon one another or pocket watches synchronize their times. Either way, it appears the concoction had the desired effect.

Being unexpectedly berated by Dr. Crutchfield was the only thing that could have made my night worse. Not a soul reacted with even a hint of concern when my curtain caught the edge of the experiment table, and not a single person had the decency to remain seated while I clawed at the floor like a house cat trying to salvage the spilled milk of an overturned saucer! Representative Howley was likely the first to leave, slithering away like the snake that he is to avoid any appearance that he had sponsored and orchestrated the entire event. Had the presentation gone well, he would have sung like a magpie to any newspaper reporter that would publish the details of his involvement.

I promise that tonight, every man, woman, and child in this city will know my work, whether they want to or not. My research will not be denied the recognition it deserves! I am Edison. I am Galileo!

E.A.

Interoffice Memorandum

Chief Cecil Miller

Raleigh Police Department

Friday, June 11, 1915

Good morning:

We must find Emory Alexander. He is
our top priority.

Following Mr. Alexander's presentation
last night, Officer Macey discovered
an unresponsive elderly man seated
near some presentation equipment that
had apparently been abandoned to
facilitate Mr. Alexander's quick and
undetected exit from the State
Capitol. After escorting Mayor
Johnson to his vehicle, Officer Macey
returned to the House Chamber to find
the elderly man sitting cross-legged
on the floor with a vacant expression
on his face, his shirt wet with what
appeared to be one of Mr. Alexander's

colorful potions. Mr. Alexander, as
well as any belongings of his that
would aid our investigation, were
nowhere to be found. Officer Macey
performed a brief search of the man's
person and found nothing that would
help to determine his identity.

After failing to elicit a response
from the man, Officer Macey
transported him to Dix Hill Hospital
for a mental health evaluation. The
man is still under evaluation at Dix
Hill. The lead physician has assured
me that, if the man regains his mental
faculties, we will be notified prior
to his release so that we can
interview him about the incident.

This is a unique case. One man, a
self-proclaimed scientist who creates
concoctions that he claims have
strange and unidentified powers, while
the other is found covered in one of
these mixtures and cannot respond to
any form of stimulus. Did the man

accidentally come into contact with the concoction? Was it thrown on him by Mr. Alexander? If so, did Mr. Alexander know that the mixture would yield such harmful results? These are the questions to which we need answers. And we need them as soon as we can get them.

Mr. Alexander's scientific research could be born from a desire to serve this community or to harm it. Until we know more about the nature of his work, we will not know which end he is seeking.

Let's find Emory Alexander, using any legal means necessary. Do not underestimate him. Expect the unexpected. Contact me with any updates.

Chief Cecil Miller

Cecil Miller

RALEIGH POLICE DEPARTMENT

**IF YOU ARE NOT A MEMBER OF THE
RALEIGH POLICE DEPARTMENT, RETURN
THIS DOCUMENT TO THE NEAREST
POLICE STATION IMMEDIATELY**

THE CAPITOL GROUNDS

Revenge, a vile, putrid thing,
can turn the heart and, with it, bring
dark thoughts of truly hurting those
who've crushed the pride and egged the nose,

Once, in this stance, a man did vie
against the state, against its high
and lofty leaders, staunchly set
t'ignore his plans, with no regret,

So through the tunnels, dark and damp,
did slink the grumbling, spiteful tramp,
beneath the strong and sturdy keep
of bills made law and deals made cheap,

Then rising through a tiled hatch
the sneak pried every door and latch,
to roam the chambers, stairs, and halls,
to wet the floors and stain the walls,

Each drop of potion briefly shined
before it sunk within its find
and prompted motion, never known,

85

to life! the cloth, the wood, the stone,

His plan complete, the burglar fled
to paths through which the hatch door led,
while in his wake the Cap'tol teemed,
a sea of life, a pride redeemed,

So mind the rails and eye the doors,
beware the stairs and watch the floors,
for, still today, the Cap'tol lives
t'avenge a wretch who ne'er forgives.

THE MANSION

A simple, evil, wretched plot
had near success, but all for naught,
for in the end the charm took hold,
but would not be a thing controll'd,

So now it creeps and roams and crawls,
among the mansion's floors and walls,
within the garden and its gates,
and through the cupboards, cups, and plates,

While harmless, it remains a fright
to see a matchless fire light,
to wander floors that roll like waves
or tame a chair that misbehaves,

Though eerie scenes and sites abound,
no resident alarms will sound,
for were the story told to all
the politic would surely fall,

As no one wants a chief or king
whose mind is frail and faltering,
who claims to head a house besieged

with portraits audibly aggrieved,

So to their graves the leaders go,
their stories of the house in tow,
that ne'er a night were out the norm,
"A banner house, in perfect form."

Interoffice Memorandum

Chief Cecil Miller

Raleigh Police Department

Monday, June 28, 1915

Good morning:

The city's problems grow worse by the day. We have found no signs of Emory Alexander since his presentation, and Judge Kays says that evidence of any criminal conduct linked to the incapacity suffered by the elderly attendee is still too circumstantial for him to sign a search warrant for Montfort Hall. Let's get him the evidence he needs! We are bound to learn more once inside the home.

I visited our elderly convalescent at Dix Hill Hospital this weekend. He remains unresponsive. The doctors believe he is improving, however, so hopefully soon we will be able to properly interview him. Who knows, he may know more about Emory Alexander than we do.

An important note: until we can interview the elderly gentleman about the incident, no one is to share anything with the press regarding our investigation. I have read enough articles and opinion pieces this year criticizing our Department's ability to respond to local crises. I do not want to fan those flames any higher with reports of an assault that occurred right under our noses.

Please note, I will be out of the office this afternoon. I received an urgent message from a State House representative who wants to discuss Mr. Alexander's presentation. My guess is he is just upset about the stained carpet in the House Chamber, but I will see what other information I can learn that may help our investigation.

Stay safe out there and wear the badge with pride.

Chief Cecil Miller

Cecil Miller

RALEIGH POLICE DEPARTMENT

IF YOU ARE NOT A MEMBER OF THE RALEIGH POLICE DEPARTMENT, RETURN THIS DOCUMENT TO THE NEAREST POLICE STATION IMMEDIATELY

THE OAK CITY GAZETTE   VOL. 1573

The Oak City Gazette

WEDNESDAY, JUNE 30, 1915

CITY ON EDGE

The city is on edge after two weeks of increased fantastic and unsettling events.

Along with claims of statue-led attacks against legislators in the State Capitol, Raleigh citizens have reported mailboxes floating, flowers biting, and sidewalks undulating. These bizarre and shocking reports make up a mere fraction of those received by the Raleigh Police Department in recent weeks.

Until late Monday afternoon, city officials were at a loss as to what might be causing the inexplicable and unnerving scenes that Raleigh citizens have grown so accustomed to since late last year. The breakthrough came during a meeting between North Carolina State House Representative Edward Howley of Dare County and Raleigh Police Chief Cecil Miller. Representative Howley confirmed Chief Miller's suspicions that all the city's recent ills stem from the scientific work of Mr. Emory Alexander of Montfort Hall, who recently, and quite infamously, failed to impress local and statewide leaders during a botched scientific presentation given in the

House Chamber of the State Capitol.

"Before agreeing to schedule the mysterious presentation," Representative Howley explained, "I insisted that Mr. Alexander briefly describe to me his research, a request which he was terribly reluctant to oblige. After he realized I would not change my mind, he relented and briefly described his work to me, speaking of potions that could 'control living and non-living objects,' causing each to act in any manner that he wished."

"Of course, in retrospect, I wish that I had not given Mr. Alexander such a large and public platform, but I felt I owed it to the people of this state to promote a presentation as potentially revolutionary as Mr. Alexander's."

Upon meeting with Representative Howley on Monday afternoon, Chief Miller immediately applied for a search warrant of Mr. Alexander's newly purchased home, Montfort Hall. The warrant would allow officers to search for evidence related to alleged charges of directed assaults against legislative and executive officials, effected by the use of scientific potions.

On Tuesday morning, after a thorough review of its contents, Wake County Superior Court Judge Robert Kays signed the warrant.

The search warrant was executed by Chief Miller and twenty other officers as the ink still dried upon its pages. Mr. Alexander was not found at his home, though officers are scouring the city in hopes of finding and questioning him at length. The Wake County Sheriff's Office and other nearby law enforcement agencies have been notified and have created their own task forces to join the manhunt.

No evidence of Mr. Alexander's scientific experiments was found during the search of Montfort Hall, a fact leading investigators to believe that his laboratory will be found in some other location. As no other property in Raleigh bears his name, Chief Miller has asked citizens to be on the lookout for any unauthorized use of sheds, barns, or other structures that could house the scientific work of Mr. Alexander.

Due to the nature of the charges against him, as well as the apparent destructive power of his scientific concoctions, Chief Miller warns that Mr. Alexander should be treated as one armed and dangerous.

THE DIARY OF EMORY ALEXANDER

The 30th Day of June, 1915. Wednesday.

I write at dawn in the laboratory.

Raleigh

I cannot believe it has come to this. Months of research

nearly ruined! Had my state-sanctioned trespassers only

looked behind the tapestry that hides my laboratory, I

would have been finished. Chief Miller could have

knocked over multiple experiments with a wave of his

hand had he been the wiser. Twenty-four hours have come

and gone, and at last I hear no more footsteps of police

officers ransacking my home.

This assault upon my work and privacy can hardly be

paralleled! I cannot allow another such intrusion. One

more search of my home and all may be lost; the

laboratory revealed and the stone discovered. Were even a basic knowledge gained of the stone, one can be sure of two things: it would not be found on any official police evidence log and, within mere days of its discovery, the Gazette would report that Chief Miller had unexpectedly resigned his post and moved states away, vaguely citing some health emergency of an extended family member. He would sell the stone to the highest bidding company, which would then use it to increase its profit a thousand times over. Or worse, he would sell it to someone who wanted to ensure that the public at large never learned of the stone or its power. It would be bad enough for a company to take credit for and undeservedly profit off of the stone, but it would be a far greater tragedy for the stone to be hidden away and never utilized by a purchaser that did not trust or understand it. I cannot allow that to happen!

In response to their attempts to halt my research by force, I must reply to my fellow citizens with something equally invasive and threatening. If I move through the city's tunnel system I will not be seen or suspected, though if I am somehow implicated, the secrecy of my route will make my involvement virtually unprovable.

While I am already a target of the Raleigh Police Department, I do not wish to turn it into an angry hornets' nest by openly challenging its officers. No, I will assault this city without it even knowing it is under attack. Tonight, as twilight slips into complete darkness, I will give the people of Raleigh my response to their provocations. My message will illuminate the night sky!

With great vengeance,

E.A.

MURPHEY SCHOOL

While teachers slept and students dreamed
a slighted, vengeful sci'ntist schemed
a plot to mar his critics' pride
before their haughty laughter died,

One night while wand'ring 'neath the ground,
a passageway, the schemer found,
this ending in a vestibule,
an ingress into Murphey School,
a school that taught the babes of power,
the target of that witching hour,

So from his bag, a match, he took,
then struck it hard upon its book,
the flame burned bright against his smile
and wrathful gaze, which eyed a vial
protruding from his open pack
that hung across his chest and back,

He pulled the flask above the flame,
then dripped the contents on the same,
it flickered once, but did not fail,
yet fell within an emerald vail

that dimmed the light and stilled the fire,
that stood as though 'twere formed with wire,

Then rising slowly 'bove the stick,
the flame blazed on, no urging wick,
it paused a moment, still as stone,
then passed into the school, alone,
and floated calmly up the stair
toward the classrooms waiting there,

Then, one by one, the flame did drift
through every doorway, ever swift,
until to master it returned,
as in its wake the whole school burned,

The sci'ntist closed his callous eyes,
while smirking lips began to rise,
then, turning hard, he slithered home,
to seethe, to dream, to strive, alone,

Still if you wander near the school,
though mended, there remains a cruel
detritus of that fateful night,
which manifests beneath moonlight,

Green flames appear and fill the halls,
then wander to the outer walls,
though siren, each will burn if touched
and maim if further held or clutched.

THE OAK CITY GAZETTE   VOL. 1575

The Oak City Gazette

FRIDAY, JULY 2, 1915

FIRE AT MURPHEY SCHOOL

Early Thursday morning, downtown Raleigh residents notified authorities of a massive fire at Murphey School, a grade school located at 443 North Person Street.

Though members of the Raleigh Fire Department's Hose Company 1 responded in minutes, hailing from nearby Station 1 on West Morgan Street, the fire was beyond control when they arrived. Fortunately, as school officials later confirmed, the building has been empty since summer recess began in June. Without the need to rescue imperiled citizens, firefighters were able to focus on mitigating property damage to the school and other surrounding structures.

Raleigh Fire Department Chief Charles Farmer spoke with reporters yesterday regarding the blaze.

"Never in my career have I seen a fire so quickly consume a building," Chief Farmer shared. "It was as if some great, invisible bellows fanned the flames, though we have found no sign of an accelerant in the rubble."

Nearby residents reported similar amazement with the speed at which the fire spread. Reports credit Mr. H. Tucker London and his wife, Mrs. Zoey London-Massey, who live on nearby Polk Street, with first reporting the blaze.

"When I noticed the fire, there were flames in only two of the school's windows," Mr. London reported. "Not twenty minutes later, the entire school was burned up!"

While Mr. London's description may sound like hyperbole, the reality is not far from his assessment. Initial reports reveal that only the outermost walls of the school remain intact following the blaze.

Firefighters neutralized the inferno just as many citizens arrived at their offices Thursday morning. Those businesses within close proximity to Murphey School were closed, however, as enormous amounts of smoke still lingered in the air over the east side of downtown.

As the sun set yesterday evening, officers with the Raleigh Police Department began to investigate the cause of the fire, suspicious that it may have been set intentionally. Raleigh Police Chief Cecil Miller has ordered his officers to canvass the neighborhood until they have spoken with every possible witness. He has also asked that any citizen with information regarding the fire contact his office immediately.

The Raleigh Police Department's investigation surrounding the fire at Murphey School, especially regarding any possible intent behind the blaze, is all the more important as Raleigh Mayor James Johnson's youngest child, Alexandra, is one of the school's current pupils.

Mayor Johnson has yet to comment publicly on the incident, though sources within his office say he has gone so far as to threaten Chief Miller with removal if he cannot bring the investigation to a swift conclusion. Mayor Johnson is reportedly fed up with the recent onslaught of unsettling and unexplained events in the capital city, which he believes creates a perception that Raleigh is unsafe and poorly managed.

One anonymous source in the Raleigh Police Department said that investigators are keen on questioning Mr. Emory Alexander of Montfort Hall.

Mr. Alexander is believed to be linked to other strange and dangerous events which have befallen the city in recent months. Even after a recent search of Mr. Alexander's home, however, his whereabouts remain a mystery to local authorities.

J. ANTON DAVIS

Interoffice Memorandum

Chief Cecil Miller

Raleigh Police Department

Saturday, July 3, 1915

Good morning:

First, note that everything found in
this memorandum is Department Eyes
Only. Any leaks to the press will
result in the immediate dismissal of
any responsible officer.

Our long season of mayhem in Raleigh
is almost over. We will soon have
Emory Alexander in our custody. I
have just returned from a final visit
to Dix Hill Hospital to see what I
could learn from the elderly gentleman
found unresponsive following Mr.
Alexander's June 10th presentation at
the State Capitol. We have had a
breakthrough.

Nurses checking the man's vital signs yesterday evening reported the sudden presence of mental lucidity from the patient, who began immediately sharing everything he could remember about himself and his many unpleasant experiences with Emory Alexander. Apparently, he has not stopped talking since.

The elderly man's name is Dr. J. Tom Crutchfield. He is a pharmacist from Asheville, North Carolina. More specifically, he is *the* pharmacist from Asheville about whom we previously received reports of his being the victim of a giant toad attack.

The suspect in Dr. Crutchfield's attack was his store helper, who investigators later learned had given the doctor the false name of Dillon Westwood and who has not been seen since the day of the attack. Dr. Crutchfield confirmed that the man who attacked him in Asheville is Raleigh's very own Emory Alexander. As to the most recent assault in the House Chamber, Dr. Crutchfield claims that Mr. Alexander threw one of his potions on him the moment he began to speak of Mr. Alexander's identity and his connection to the attack in Asheville.

I have confirmed with the Asheville Police Department that Mr. Alexander is still wanted for questioning and eventual charges in Buncombe County in relation to the toad attack. With this information, I will request another search warrant for Montfort Hall from Judge Kays. There must be something in that home that will lead us to Emory Alexander, and with Dr. Crutchfield's testimony regarding Mr. Alexander's fugitive status we now have all the evidence that we need to pursue him until he is in our custody.

We will serve the warrant tomorrow morning as citizens of our community are busy preparing for their Fourth of July celebrations. Every member of the force must be at headquarters and ready to go by 0700. Remember as we

prepare for this operation that Mr.
Alexander is to be treated as armed
and extremely dangerous.

Two final points: any documents found
within Montfort Hall containing plans
or ingredient lists for potions or
other scientific concoctions are to be
immediately sealed and brought
directly to me. Due to the dangerous
nature of the information in such
documents, they will be marked for
Chief's Eyes Only. Second, the Mayor
has requested to take part in this
operation, so we will need a few
officers to remain outside with him
once we have entered the home. He is
not to enter Montfort Hall until a
full security sweep is complete. You
can blame me if the Mayor protests.

That is all for now. Everyone except
those listed as essential personnel
should take the day off and rest up
for tomorrow morning. Let's show this
city and its resident potion-brewing
fugitive what the Raleigh Police force
is made of!

Wear your badge, each of you, with courage and pride.

Chief Cecil Miller

Cecil Miller

RALEIGH POLICE DEPARTMENT

IF YOU ARE NOT A MEMBER OF THE RALEIGH POLICE DEPARTMENT, RETURN THIS DOCUMENT TO THE NEAREST POLICE STATION IMMEDIATELY

THE DIARY OF EMORY ALEXANDER

The 3rd Day of July, 1915. Saturday.

I write by night in the laboratory.

Raleigh

It has come to this. I have no other choice. Every day that passes is one day closer to the discovery of my laboratory and the destruction or theft of my work.

The people of Raleigh clearly fear what they do not understand, just as Dr. Crutchfield did. Why did I believe they would be any different? My naiveté leaves me now burned a second time for reaching toward the fire; that warm, enticing fire of community. For those like me, such flames hold no comfort, but only serve as a reminder that we are not free to share in the fire's warmth. It is not that we are chilled by such exclusion, but that we are the chilled air itself. We are the cold. Different from the others, dissimilar in basic substance. No matter. At least I now see these truths clearly.

I did not want to introduce the final phase of my research until the public was comfortable with its less controversial concepts, but it must now be done. Any hesitation and I could be stopped in my tracks as I round the final turn. For ill or for gain, I will force myself to the finish line.

The greatest possible impact of my potions, that of giving humans superhuman qualities, must be shown to the people of Raleigh, not explained. Humans will soon possess the best and most useful qualities of animals, rocks, plants, and any other object, needing only one sip of a properly mixed formula to turn dreams once thought to be impossible into reality. From medicine to manual labor, these potions will revolutionize every aspect of the human experience.

It is regrettable that I have not had the opportunity to properly test this, the greatest of my hypotheses, but it appears that my experimentation will begin tonight, with me as the first subject. The logic is sound and my formulas show no signs of error. Similar tests on animals have succeeded with spectacular results.

In case of an accident, let it be known to any who find this diary that it will be the qualities of a red wolf that I intend to manifest by drinking the potion that now sits on the table before me. This infusion should increase my strength and speed, as well as the force of my bite. No other effects should be readily apparent.

It is fitting that, on the eve of our nation's birth, a new era of human achievement and progress will be born!

To health. To success. To progress!

With great hope and perseverance,

E.A.

THE OAK CITY GAZETTE   VOL. 1578

The Oak City Gazette

MONDAY, JULY 5, 1915

FUGITIVE SLAIN

Local authorities have finally discovered the fate of the infamous scientist, Mr. Emory Alexander, who had been a fugitive from the law since last June. Mr. Alexander had been charged with assault and arson for crimes allegedly occurring during his brief time in Raleigh, as well as attempted murder stemming from an incident that occurred when he was previously living in Asheville, North Carolina.

Sunday morning, while on regular patrol for the Fourth of July holiday, Wake County Sheriff's Deputy William D. McConaghay observed the front door to Mr. Alexander's manor hanging by one hinge, appearing to have been forcibly opened.

"While I secured the perimeter of the home, Chief Miller, Mayor Johnson, and the entire Raleigh Police Department arrived with a search warrant in hand," Deputy McConaghay explained. "We surrounded the home, secured all the exits, and entered through the broken front door with our firearms drawn."

Deputy McConaghay and the other members of the search

party found torn paintings, splintered furniture, and every manner of Mr. Alexander's personal effects scattered throughout the home.

"The strangest thing," Deputy McConaghay added, "wasn't that the home had been ransacked, but that every nook and notch of the place held tufts of thick, brown hair, like something from a dog or wolf."

After continuing their search throughout the manor, Raleigh Police Officer Henry J. Davis made the most notable discovery when he pulled back the slivers of a tattered tapestry that hung in Mr. Alexander's cellar.

Officer Davis reportedly discovered a hidden room, approximately three hundred square feet in size, that appeared to have been dug out of the earth beyond the basement wall. The room was filled with shattered beakers, overturned experiment tables, and a small wooden desk. Officer Davis had

stumbled upon what has been eluding local authorities for months; the scientific laboratory of Mr. Emory Alexander.

Atop the desk sat a dark blue diary bearing Mr. Alexander's name. Under specific orders, Officer Davis immediately took the diary to Raleigh Police Chief Cecil Miller. It reportedly remains in Chief Miller's personal custody, held as criminal evidence and deemed too dangerous for dissemination to the public at large or even throughout his own department.

Speaking anonymously, various officers who briefly observed the diary during the initial search have confirmed that it contains detailed accounts of Mr. Alexander's journey to Raleigh, as well as the nature and history of his scientific experimentation.

Mr. Alexander, himself, is believed to be deceased, the victim of an attack by wolves or wild dogs that found some manner of ingress to his home. Though the scientist's body was not recovered, his clothes, undergarments, and personal effects were found shredded to pieces on the dirt floor of his laboratory.

A source within the Raleigh Police Department admitted that no blood was found at the scene, noting this fact as odd considering the apparent manner in which Mr. Alexander died. This information has led many to speculate that Chief Miller and the City of Raleigh have not been completely transparent as to the nature and progress of the ongoing investigation.

It is not known whether Mr. Alexander is survived by any relatives, though sources within the investigation claim to have learned important information about his origins from his diary.

As the purpose and nature of Mr. Alexander's brief time in Raleigh are still a matter of criminal investigation, no further facts regarding the search of his home have been released.

Following the incident, Mayor Johnson announced that Montfort Hall would immediately come under the authority of the City of Raleigh, more specifically, under the direct supervision of the Mayor's Office. Mayor Johnson's announcement alluded to historical precedent for such action, though press requests for proof of that precedent have so far gone unanswered.

J. ANTON DAVIS

Interoffice Memorandum

Chief Cecil Miller

Raleigh Police Department

Monday, July 5, 1915

Good morning:

Due to recent, unfortunate events
concerning the health of various
extended family members of mine, I am
resigning my post as Chief of the
Raleigh Police Department. My
resignation is effective immediately.

I will be moving away from the Raleigh
area and will not be immediately
reachable. I will send the Department
my contact information as soon as I am
able to do so.

Thank you for your service and for
your commitment to the citizens of
this great city and state. It has

been an honor serving alongside each
of you.

Be safe, be brave, and remember the
badge you wear.

Chief Cecil Miller

Cecil Miller

RALEIGH POLICE DEPARTMENT

**IF YOU ARE NOT A MEMBER OF THE
RALEIGH POLICE DEPARTMENT, RETURN
THIS DOCUMENT TO THE NEAREST
POLICE STATION IMMEDIATELY**

J. ANTON DAVIS

THE WEREWOLF ON DIX HILL

There is a tale as old as stone,
which has been passed by word alone,
of man and beast, together bound,
not truly man, nor fully hound,

A site that's sure to paralyze,
the fangs, the fur, the claws, the eyes
that none would say were different than
those found in woman or in man,
yet fierce and grey and ever wild,
and vacant, as a man beguiled,

It roams the hills just west of town,
yet, often, does it venture down,
among the houses, shops, and streets,
though in the shad'wy dark it keeps
well out of sight of friend or foe,
all likely in the latter, though,

If ever did one glimpse its face,
the city whole would join the chase,
until its head was mounted high,
before a soul could wonder why

the eyes and mind, the size and gait,
had, eerily, a hum'nly trait,
though held within a wild brute,
each shows a sign of man at root,

But none may ever know the plot
of time before the beast was not
the monster that it is today,
a poor, enchanted runaway,

So e'er it prowls the lonely nights,
among the town and in the heights,
until it's caught, and either slain
or one divines what isn't plain.

THE
END

ACKNOWLEDGEMENTS

While I know it is always difficult for writers to craft a worthy list of individuals to acknowledge at the end of a book, I assume it is an even more daunting task when the book in question has been written over multiple years, as was *Oak City Tales.* With that said, I want to thank everyone, named and unnamed, who helped edit and design this book and who listened to me dream aloud as I talked through this project the past four-and-a-half years.

Thank you to my wife, Alexandra, who has encouraged me to complete this book since I first began writing it back in January 2017. She loves this story just as much as I do, and its completion and any of its merits are due in large part to her encouragement and editing prowess.

Thank you to my father, John, and mother, Kathy, who have taught me from a young age to dream and wonder. Their critiques and thoughts were invaluable in writing this book. They each have literary minds and understand the power and poignancy of a well-told story, which I hope they have found within these pages.

Thank you to my father-in-law, Ed, and mother-in-law, Laurie, who have heard these stories since the moment of their inception and have shared incredibly helpful critiques and ideas throughout the book's writing process.

Thank you to my friend and de facto editor, Dillon Lunn, who worked with me through the meat of creating and formatting this book before I told him I wanted to put it on hold to first publish *Love is: A former magistrate's poetic reflections on love and marriage in a county courthouse*, a book of poems I published in the fall of 2020. Dillon's practical and industry insight, gained from publishing his first novel, *The Kingdom v. John Reid*, was invaluable.

Lastly, thank you to my many beta readers, both family and friends, who helped me get this book across the finish line.

AUTHOR BIOGRAPHY

J. Anton Davis is a husband, father, attorney, author, and poet. A born-and-raised North Carolinian, he lives in Raleigh with his wife, Alexandra, and sons, James and Liam.

Though Davis has written poetry and fiction privately for twenty years, he launched his website, JAntonPoetry.com, in 2019 to begin sharing his writing publicly.

Beyond writing poetry and fiction, Davis enjoys exploring local Greenway trails, playing soccer, and spending time with his family and friends.

J. Anton, James, Alexandra, and Liam
Fall 2021

FOLLOW THE AUTHOR

Keep up with the writings of J. Anton Davis by following these five steps:

- o Visit his website, JAntonPoetry.com.
- o While at his website, sign up for the J. Anton Poetry e-Newsletter.
- o Follow @jantonpoetry on Instagram
- o Like the J. Anton Poetry Facebook page.
- o Email him at JAntonPoetry@gmail.com to let him know what you thought of *Oak City Tales*.

If you enjoyed this book, remember to leave a review on Amazon.com and Goodreads.com. Also, don't forget to tell your friends, family, and social media connections about it, and let your local bookstores know that you would like to see works by J. Anton Davis on their shelves.

Thank you for reading!

ISBN: 978-1-7355407-2-6 (Paperback)
ISBN: 978-1-7355407-3-3 (eBook)

OAK CITY TALES CHECKLIST

Go with family and friends to visit* and learn more about the history of these Raleigh sites that feature prominently in *Oak City Tales*:

o Boylan Bridge
o Dorothea Dix Park
o Fayetteville Street
o Historic City Market
o Historic Montfort Hall
o Historic Murphey School
o Historic Oakwood Neighborhood
o Moore Square
o Nash Square
o The North Carolina State Capitol
o The North Carolina Governor's Mansion
o Union Station

* While each of these locations is publicly owned or listed in a public register of historic places, please note that the days and times one may visit these sites may differ, and all or part of these sites may not be open to the public at all.

OTHER WORKS BY J. ANTON DAVIS

Love is: A former magistrate's poetic reflections on love and marriage in a county courthouse

The memories found in this collection of poems are all firsthand accounts of love shared between couples, family, friends, and even strangers, all set in the context of a North Carolina civil wedding ceremony. From 2013 to 2019, J. Anton Davis served as a North Carolina Magistrate Judge in Raleigh, North Carolina. From his ninth-floor courtroom in the towering Wake County Justice Center, he performed nearly 6,000 civil wedding ceremonies. While there are countless stories Davis could share from his tenure as a magistrate, *Love is* focuses on the most memorable aspect of the many ceremonies he officiated: love.

JAntonPoetry.com

JAntonPoetry.com is the official home for the writings of J. Anton Davis and contains over 100 poems written by Davis.

Made in the USA
Coppell, TX
20 July 2023

19405115R00090